Best friends

■SCHOLASTIC

Scholastic Children's Books,
Euston House,
24 Eversholt Street,
London NW1 1DB, UK

A division of Scholastic Ltd
London ~ New York ~ Toronto ~ Sydney ~ Auckland
Mexico City ~ New Delhi ~ Hong Kong

First published in the UK by Scholastic Ltd, 2019

Text © Scholastic, 2019
Illustrations by Helen Chapman © Scholastic, 2019
Produced for Scholastic by Plum5 Ltd

ISBN 978 1407 19377 9

Printed and bound in the UK by Bell and Bain Ltd, Glasgow

2 4 6 8 10 9 7 5 3 1

This journal belongs to:

Sadhbh

Packed with activities, makes, bakes and fill-in fun, this is the perfect journal to share with your bestie!

Let's get started!

All about me

Use these pages to introduce yourself.

My first name: *Sadhbh*

My surname: *leanard*

My nickname: *Sadhbh*

My age: *9*

My birthday: *26\8\2013*

My shoe size: *2*

My hair colour: *blaand*

Draw a picture of yourself or stick in a selfie here:

All about my bestie

Use these pages to introduce your bestie.

Best friend's name: Ciara

Their surname: O Siulliivain

Their nickname: Ciara

Their age: 8

Their birthday: 14\14\2014

Their shoe size: $2\frac{1}{2}$

Their hair colour: gold

Draw a picture of your best friend or stick in a photo of them here:

January: endless possibilities

January is all about new beginnings, trying out new things, and setting goals for the rest of the year. Fill in these pages with all the exciting new things you'd like to try out with your best friend this year.

JANUARY

New hairstyle
What I liked about it was:

....

....

FEBRUARY

New food
What I liked about it was:

....

....

MARCH

New sport
What I liked about it was:

....

....

APRIL

New hobby
What I liked about it was:

....

....

MAY

New book
What I liked about it was:

....

....

JUNE

New language
What I liked about it was:

....

....

JULY

New fruit
What I liked about it was:

....

....

AUGUST

New vegetable
What I liked about it was:

....

....

SEPTEMBER

New band/song
What I liked about it was:

....

....

OCTOBER

New after-school club
What I liked about it was:

....

....

NOVEMBER

New style
What I liked about it was:

....

....

DECEMBER

New film
What I liked about it was:

....

....

What colour is your personality?

Have you ever thought about what
colour would match your personality?
Take this quiz to find out whether you're
a vibrant red or a mellow yellow!

A large group of friends –
I love hanging out with lots
of people

You would
rather have...

One best friend – I would
rather be close to one person
and tell them all my secrets

Y

START

Do you make
decisions easily?

English – I spend lots of time
reading and thinking about
characters from books

N

Your favourite
subject is...

Maths – I like figuring things
out logically to find solutions
to problems

Yellow

You are relaxed and friendly. Your outgoing personality means you love to be the life and soul of the party.

Do you like being busy all the time?

N

Y

Red

You are strong and loyal. With your determined and focused attitude, you succeed in whatever you put your mind to.

Do you daydream a lot?

N

Y

Purple

You are imaginative and creative. With your artistic spirit and openness to try new things, you communicate well with everyone around you.

Would you wear a dress over jeans?

N

Y

Blue

You are calm and thoughtful. With your cool head and rational mind, all your friends come to you for your great advice.

15

February:
forever friends

Grab your best friend and play this fun game! First, tick your answers, then ask your bestie to do the same on the opposite page and see how similar you are.
No peeking!

Would you rather...

be a famous athlete ☑ or a famous inventor ☐ ?

be able to teleport ☑ or become invisible ☐ ?

eat ice cream ☐ or pizza ☑ ?

have wings ☑ or a unicorn horn ☐ ?

be an amazing dancer ☐ or a talented singer ☑ ?

have a fear of heights ☐ or a fear of the dark ☑ ?

Would you rather:

be a famous athlete ☐ or a famous inventor ☐ ?

be able to teleport ☐ or become invisible ☐ ?

eat ice cream ☐ or pizza ☐ ?

have wings ☐ or a unicorn horn ☐ ?

be an amazing dancer ☐ or a talented singer ☐ ?

have a fear of heights ☐ or a fear of the dark ☐ ?

Valentine's bake

Valentine's Day is all about sharing the love! Whether you're spending the day with friends or family, these delicious heart-shaped love bugs will make the perfect treats.

You will need:

- 175 g plain flour
- 100 g chilled butter, cubed
- 85 g icing sugar
- 1 tsp vanilla extract
- 1 egg yolk
- red food colouring
- black food colouring
- 100 g icing sugar
- edible pearly ball decorations (optional)
- a heart-shaped cookie cutter

Method:

1. Line two baking trays with baking paper and ask an adult to preheat the oven to 180°C.
2. Mix the flour, butter, sugar, vanilla and egg yolk. Slowly add water until it forms a dough.

3. Tip the dough on to a work surface and knead, then wrap in cling film and chill for 20 mins.

4. Roll out the dough and use the heart-shaped cutter to cut out heart shapes. Place on baking trays and bake for 12 mins until golden and then leave to cool.

5. Mix the icing sugar with water until you get a thick paste and then split between two bowls. Add red food colouring to the first bowl and black food colouring to the second bowl. Pour the icing into piping bags (or use a small sandwich bag and snip off the corner).

6. Use the red icing for your love bug cookie's body. Use the black icing to give it a head at the pointy end and a line down the centre to give it wings. Use the rest of the black icing to add spots, then leave to set.

March: marvellous makeover

Whether your style is more glitz and glam or comfy and cosy, makeovers are super fun when you're doing them with your favourite friend.

Draw your best friend a dream outfit you think they would love here:

Now, switch! Give them a chance to design
an amazing outfit for you here:

Grab more
paper and come
up with more
amazing outfits
for each other!

Furry fashion icon

Which of these adorable animals do you get your fashion inspo from without even knowing it? Take this fab flow chart quiz to find out.

START

Do you prefer to wear bright colours or dark colours?

bright →

dark

summer

Do you prefer summer or winter style?

Do you have a similar style to your friends?

yep

nope

winter

What's more important – being comfortable or looking stylish?

comfort

style

Flamingo
Bright colours and fun prints fill your wardrobe – just like a funky flamingo, you're not afraid to stand out from the crowd!

Sparkly T-shirt or cuddly cardigan?

T-shirt

cardigan

Llama
Like these super-cute creatures, your style is comfy and cosy. Fluffy jumpers and earthy colours are your fave things to wear.

hat

Woolly hat or statement necklace?

necklace

Narwhal
Your look is super-unique, just like a narwhal's! You have your own style and you're not too fussed about following fashion.

April: beautiful bunting

What better way for you and your bestie to jazz up your bedrooms than with matching beautiful bunting!

You will need:

- A4 card (or paper) in your favourite colours
- string
- scissors
- a glue stick
- ruler (optional)

Method:

1. Cut a triangle about the size of ¾ of the paper.
2. Grab your string and lay it out. Make sure to leave about a foot of string on each end so that you can hang your bunting when you are done!
3. Fold about 2 cm of the base of your triangle over the string (feel free to use a ruler!).
4. Grab your glue and glue down the fold with the string in the crease of the fold.
5. Repeat these steps until you have a variety of triangles hanging from the string.
6. Hang up your hand-made beautiful bunting!

If you're feeling confident, try different shapes like stars or hearts!

Cool continent quiz

The world is a pretty big place. There are so many amazing things to see and so many different people to meet. Take this quiz to discover the continent you should travel to next.

1. Pick an adorable animal:
   a) Sloth   b) Panda   c) Moose   d) Giraffe

2. Pick a delicious fruit:
   a) Passion fruit   b) Mango
   c) Blueberry   d) Watermelon

3. Pick a holiday activity:
   a) Hanging out at the beach
   b) Exploring cultural attractions
   c) Shopping and sightseeing
   d) Spotting lots of wildlife

4. Pick a musical instrument:
   a) Maracas   b) Flute   c) Electric guitar   d) Drums

5. Pick a beautiful bird:
   a) Toucan   b) Crane   c) Eagle   d) Ostrich

Mostly As – South America

Sunny South America has some of the most beautiful beaches in the world! Go trekking in Peru, dance in a Brazilian carnival and see the world's biggest waterfall in Venezuela.

Mostly Bs – Asia

Discover incredible ancient history and visit some of the world's busiest cities in awesome Asia! Walk the Great Wall of China, try karaoke in Japan and explore the paradise islands of Thailand.

Mostly Cs – North America

There's so much to see and do in amazing North America! Go skiing in Canada, take a road trip across the USA and visit the sites of ancient civilizations in Mexico.

Mostly Ds – Africa

From its national parks to its cool coastlines, incredible Africa has so much to offer! Go on safari in Tanzania, journey across the dunes in Morocco and climb a mountain in South Africa.

May: book bonanza

Time to write a smash-hit story – but first you need the perfect title!

Check out the lists below then choose how many pets you have and the first letter of your name to discover what you should call your story.

For example, if you have no pets and your first name starts with the letter 'A', your story will be called 'The Indigo Unicorn'.

Number of pets

0 – The Indigo

1 – The Brave

2 – The Brilliant

3 – The Mysterious

4 – The Bright

5 – The Wonderful

6 – The Suspicious

7 – The Miniature

8 – The Giant

9 – The Courageous

10 – The Invisible

11+ – The Strange

First letter of your first name

A – Unicorn	N – Restaurant
B – House	O – Doctor
C – Lady	P – Project
D – Catastrophe	Q – Delivery
E – Gentleman	R – Night
F – Hat	S – Handshake
G – Stranger	T – Crystal
H – Van	U – Trifle
I – Adventure	V – Teacher
J – Storm	W – Dance
K – Holiday	X – Goat
L – Job	Y – Destiny
M – Friendship	Z – Toadstool

The title of my story is:

Story time

Write the opening to an exciting story below. You could use the title quiz from the previous page to inspire you.

....

....

....

....

....

....

....

....

....

Find your flower quiz

Spring is here! Find out what flower each of your friends is most like with this quiz.

START

Springtime is here! How do you feel?

→ Just okay. → Why?
- Autumn and winter mean cosy times. Why say goodbye?
- Still a while until things really warm up. April showers anyone?

→ Yay! Yay! Yay! → Why?
- Longer days mean more time to get out and have fun!
- It means summer isn't far behind! Bring on the sunshine!

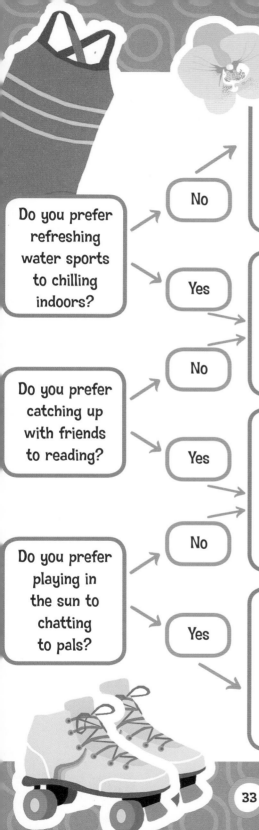

Precious orchid

Delicate and beautiful, you're a gal who prefers to relax in the shade or even better by a warm fireside. Roll on autumn!

Water lily

You're a flower that prefers still waters to making a splash. A chilled chica, warmer weather means cooling off by the pool.

Rambling rose

Spring is here and it is blooming marvellous. Like a rose you are bold, beautiful and enjoy the sunshine surrounded by your fun-loving friends.

Sunny daisy

Like a daisy you are open, fun and love the sunshine. You can handle whatever the weather throws at you but prefer the bright days of spring and summer.

Do you prefer refreshing water sports to chilling indoors? — No / Yes

Do you prefer catching up with friends to reading? — No / Yes

Do you prefer playing in the sun to chatting to pals? — No / Yes

Food favourites

Do you get excited thinking about marvellous meals and yummy snacks? Fill in all about you and your best friend's food faves below!

My favourite meal is:

....

My best friend's favourite meal is:

....

My favourite drink is:

....

My best friend's favourite drink is:

....

My favourite fruit is:

....

My best friend's favourite fruit is:

....

My favourite chocolate bar is:

....

My best friend's favourite chocolate bar is:

....

MILK
OLATE

Draw your dream picnic here.
Add all the delicious snacks and drinks
you and your bestie would pack!

July:
very berry banana blast smoothie

You will need:

- 1 banana
- 227 g mixed berries
- 350 ml of milk
- 76 g Greek yoghurt (optional)
- 2 teaspoons honey (optional)

Method:

1. With help from an adult, carefully slice the banana.
2. Ask an adult to put your mixed berries and freshly sliced banana into a blender.
3. Add the milk (you can also add yoghurt and honey now if you want to!) and blend until thick and creamy.
4. Pour smoothie mixture into a glass.
5. Decorate with any leftover fruit!

Top tip: to make enough for you and your bestie, just double the ingredients!

Stick a picture of your amazing smoothie here:

Friendship bracelets

You will need:

- thread in three colours
- scissors
- sellotape

①

Cut the threads to the same length as from your shoulder to your fingertips.

②

Tie them together in a knot. Tape the end to a flat surface.

③

Knot the far-left thread (blue) to the next thread along (yellow), by taking the left thread over the top of the second thread. Pull until the knot moves up to the top of the yellow thread. Pull it tight. Repeat, tying the blue over the yellow again.

④

Tie the first (blue) thread around the third (pink) thread. Pull tight to the top in a knot. Do this one more time.

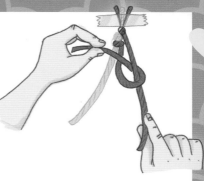

⑤

Repeat steps 3 and 4, knotting the left-hand thread to the middle thread twice and then to the right-hand thread twice.

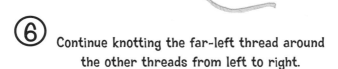

⑥

Continue knotting the far-left thread around the other threads from left to right.

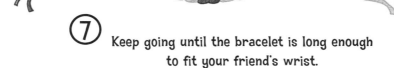

⑦

Keep going until the bracelet is long enough to fit your friend's wrist.

⑧

Tie a knot in the end and trim any excess thread. Tie the bracelet on to your friend's wrist!

August:
dream holiday

Are you a beach lover or an adventure seeker? Take this quiz to find out what kind of holiday would suit you best!

1. What's your favourite holiday season?
a) Summer b) Autumn c) Spring d) Winter

2. What's your ideal holiday outfit?
a) A swimsuit and shorts b) A jacket and walking boots
c) Jeans and sandals d) A long dress and a floppy hat

3. What's in your holiday backpack?
a) A pair of sunglasses b) An umbrella
c) A map d) A water bottle

4. What's your holiday hairstyle?
a) Loose and wavy b) In a high ponytail
c) Short and styled d) In braids

5. What's on your holiday playlist?
a) Current charts music b) Your favourite band
c) Interesting classical music d) Something new and undiscovered

6. What's your holiday read?
a) A funny story b) The local newspaper
c) Your guidebook d) An action adventure

7. What's your fave holiday activity?
a) Relaxing in the sun b) Going for a picnic
c) Visiting a museum d) Going horse riding

8. What would you most like to eat on holiday?
a) Ice cream b) Fudge c) Pizza d) Seafood

Mostly As
You are a beach lover! With your bright swimming gear and surf shorts, your dream destination involves sun, sea and sand.

Mostly Bs
You are a countryside explorer! An ideal holiday for you involves going for long walks, admiring the scenery and spending as much time outside as possible.

Mostly Cs
You are a cool city traveller! Forget the quiet of the countryside, the bright lights of a busy place are where you want to spend your time.

Mostly Ds
You are an adventure seeker! It doesn't matter if it's a scary sport, a new food or a quirky outfit, you are always keen to do something different on holiday.

Bumper BFF quiz!

How well do you know your best friend?

Take this quiz to find out whether you're completely connected or if you need to brush up on your friend facts. Fill in your answers below, then ask your best friend to mark it for you.

You get 1 point for each answer you get right.

Fill in your best friend's...

Eye colour:

....

Middle name:

....

Height:

....

Biggest fear:

....

Star sign:

....

Favourite band/song:

....

Favourite animal:

....

Favourite colour:

....

Favourite hobbies:

1. ....

2. ....

3. ....

Favourite season:

....

Favourite TV show:

....

Favourite book:

....

Favourite meal:

....

Favourite dessert:

....

Dream job:

....

Top 5 dream places to visit:

1. ....

2. ....

3. ....

4. ....

5. ....

- Mark your quiz and see how well you know your best friend!

0-4: Friendship fuzzy
You know the essential info, but you need to find out more to show how close you are. Ask her to tell you her answers so you know for next time.

5-10: Warming up
Firm friends! You two hang out all the time and you're clearly up to date with her likes and dislikes. Keep asking questions so you can discover more and more things about her.

11-15: Mind reader
When it comes to friends, you two are the best of the best! Either you have super powers (unlikely) or you're just so close that you always know what your best friend is thinking. Your BFF is lucky to have you!

MILK
CHOCOLATE

September: school days

Whether school is a minor yawn or a major yay, you spend a lot of time in the classroom. Fill these pages with your thoughts about all things school.

Draw a picture of things you'd find in your backpack here:

Favourite subjects:

1. ....

2. ....

3. ....

4. ....

5. ....

Favourite teacher:

....

Favourite after-school club:

....

At break you'll find me:

....

At lunch you'll find me:

....

....

....

Pot of gold

Going back to school can be exciting but stressful, which is why it's great to have friends to motivate you!

Follow the simple steps below to create a 'pot of gold' for your best friend, full of reminders of how awesome they are. This way, even when you're not around, you're still their biggest cheerleader!

You will need:

- a jar
- glue
- coloured paper
- a pen
- sequins or other decorations

Top tip: you can also add their favourite sayings, jokes or song lyrics to keep things interesting!

Steps:

1. Tear the coloured paper into strips.
2. Write a lovely compliment or motivational phrase on the strip of paper.
3. Fold up the piece of paper and put it in the jar.
4. Repeat these steps until the jar is full.
5. Decorate the outside of the jar with anything that reminds you of your bestie. This can be a simple bow made of coloured string, or glitter and sequins!

Stick a picture of your
pot of gold here:

49

October: fancy-dress fun

Dressing up for Halloween can be just as fun as collecting all the candy. Double the fun by co-ordinating your outfit with your bestie!

Some ideas:

- good witch/bad witch
- superhero duo
- mythical creatures
- book characters
- movie or TV show characters
- favourite animals

Design both your costumes here:

51

Cosy cups

Get cosy after kicking leaves in the park with these warming drinks.

Warm spiced apple drink
(serves two)

You will need:
- 500 ml apple juice
- ½ tsp cinnamon and nutmeg
- zest of an orange
- cinnamon sticks to serve

How to make:
1. Pour the apple juice into a pan and add the spices and zest.
2. Ask an adult to help you warm it on the hob. Do not let it boil.
3. Carefully pour the warm apple juice into two cups.
4. Pop a cinnamon stick into each cup and serve. Apple-tastic!

Rich hot chocolate

(serves two)

Top tip: sprinkle marshmallows on top for an even tastier treat.

You will need:

- 400 ml milk
- 50 ml cream
- 80 g dark chocolate chips

How to make:

1. Pour the milk and cream into a microwaveable jug.

2. Pop the jug in the microwave for 2 ½ minutes. Watch the milk through the window to make sure it doesn't boil.

3. Ask an adult to take the jug out of the microwave.

4. Add the chocolate chips and stir until they have melted into the milk and cream.

5. Pour into two cups and enjoy!

What's your music style?

Is it all about a catchy chorus or a big guitar solo? Answer these questions to reveal your music style. Don't forget to try out this awesome quiz on your friends too!

1. Why do you listen to music?
a) I love singing along b) I like dancing to it
c) It helps me relax d) Music is my passion

2. What's most important for you in a song?
a) The lyrics should tell a story
b) A catchy chorus and a good beat to dance to
c) The vocals – I love listening to amazing harmonies
d) The way the instruments are played

3. What performance would you most like to see?
a) A top West End show
b) A pop star's sellout tour
c) A famous choir
d) An edgy rock band

4. Do you fancy trying out a music festival one day?
a) Theatre is more my thing
b) Is there pop music? I'm in
c) I don't like crowds
d) Camping and cool bands? Yes, please

Mostly As

You're a musical theatre enthusiast and you truly believe that nothing beats a big show tune. Your perfect Sunday afternoon would be spent singing along to *Grease* or *Mary Poppins*.

Mostly Bs

Pure pop is the only music for you! You know the words to all the hottest chart hits and think karaoke is the best invention ever. Music is all about having fun and you love a tune with a catchy chorus.

Mostly Cs

You're all about music that helps you. You love everything from folk to classical and you appreciate good choir vocals too. Nothing beats chilling out to music when you've had a tiring day at school.

Mostly Ds

You are a music geek! If your pals want to know anything about a famous band or talented guitarist, they'll always turn to you. It's all about rock music for you – the louder the better.

Outdoor activity quiz

Find out what kind of activity will get you racing off into the great outdoors.

START

Do you like heights?

No way! → Why?

- Who likes falling? No thank you.
- Getting up and down seems too much like hard work.

Absolutely! → Why?

- There's so much more to see than there is on the ground.
- You love the idea of whizzing down from them. It's like flying!

Merry mermaid

From surfing to scuba diving, there's always something fun to do in the ocean. Why not see if you can join a local swimming club to perfect your skills for your next ocean adventure?

No

Do you prefer lying on the sand to swimming in the ocean?

Yes

Happy camper

Getting outdoors doesn't have to be hard work. Grab a book and a blanket, or string up your hammock and enjoy some fresh air without even breaking a sweat.

No

Do you like walks in the countryside?

Yes

Head for hikes

Pack a bag with a yummy picnic, and go for a nature hike with your family. Even if you live in the city, a little bit of countryside is never too far away. Get out there!

No

Do you like ice and snow?

Yes

Ski you later

You've got a head for heights, a need for speed and are ready for the mountains. Find out if there is a dry ski slope near you to hone your skills.

December: festive fun

Christmas is a time for family, friends, food and fun! What are you and your bestie up to over the holidays? Write all about your celebrations here.

For Christmas this year we would like:

....

Our favourite festive foods are:

....

Our top five Christmas songs are:

1. ....

2. ....

3. ....

4. ....

5. ....

Our top three Christmas movies are:

1. ....

2. ....

3. ....

Our favourite holiday game is:

....

We think the best part of Christmas Day is:

....

....

Beautiful bookmarks

Whether you prefer reading curled up in bed or spread out in the garden enjoying the lovely sunshine, a bookmark always comes in handy.

Follow the simple steps below to create matching bookmarks for you and your bestie – and never lose your page again!

You will need:

- two different coloured pieces of card
- string
- scissors
- ruler
- glitter glue

Get an adult to help you!

Steps:

1. Cut out a rectangle shape from the first piece of card, about 20 cm in length and 3 cm in width.
2. Using the second piece of card, cut out stars in different sizes.
3. Decorate your rectangle bookmark with the stars and use the glitter glue to design your own decorations.
4. Enjoy reading!

What would you change about your favourite book cover –
would you give it a new title? An entirely new look?
Grab your best friend and recreate one of your
favourite covers here:

What a year!

Another year over... and what a year it's been! Write down all your favourite memories, so they'll stay with you forever.

The most surprising thing that happened this year was:

....

....

....

The thing I'm most proud of is:

....

....

....

The best day of the whole year was:

....

....

....